Zaida Baby

My First Keepsake

preserving precious memories
from pregnancy to first birthday

Library and Archives Canada Cataloguing in Publication

Zaida baby : my first keepsake / Sandy Jamieson.

ISBN 978-0-9780857-0-4

1. Baby books. I. Title.

HQ779.J33 2007   649′.122   C2007-903596-5

© Mixed Sources · Sources Mixtes
Product group from well-managed forests,
controlled sources and recycled wood or fiber
Groupe de produits issu de forêts bien gérées,
de sources contrôlées et de bois ou fibres recyclés
www.fsc.org Cert no. SW-COC-002458
© 1996 Forest Stewardship Council
FSC
10%

Zaida Baby

My First Keepsake

This book is for: _____

With love: _____

preserving precious memories
from pregnancy to first birthday

Special Thanks

Friends often provide encouragement, even through the simplest of
conversations. I would like to thank Nanci for being
integral to the thought process of "Zaida Baby — My First Keepsake".

My sincerest gratitude goes out to Caitlin, Brandi, Krista,
Shakira and Beckie, with whom I debated numerous ideas.
Your listening ears and advice are greatly appreciated!

To Mom, Dad and Cyndi for supporting my decisions.

To Don, Keri, Faye, Karen and Tammy:
Thank you for your feedback and suggestions.

To Emily, the angel that provided me with guidance.

To Chadwick for your generous assistance.
I recognize your knowledge, ingeniousness, infinite
patience, and love. You're amazing and motivating.

And finally,
to all the babies, mothers, fathers, brothers, sisters and grandparents:
Thank you for your contribution to this book.
I couldn't have done it without you.

Zaida Baby

- introduction — 007

- definition of zaida — 009

- the story of 'zaida baby' — 011

- from a parent's perspective — 017

- pregnancy journal — 095

- from a baby's perspective — 109

introduction

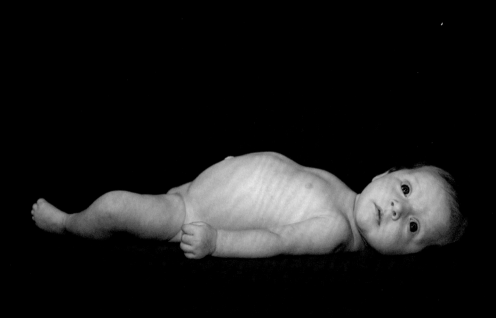

<u>word</u>: zaida

<u>definition</u>: fortunate

<u>language</u>: arabic

<u>translation</u>: fortunate baby

a v e r y   z a i d a   l o u i s e

Zaida Baby

Avery Zaida Louise was the first of four children born to Caitlin
and Rick. Caitlin was notified by a doctor that she may never
have children. She was then treated with a LEEP procedure
(Loop Electrosurgical Excision Procedure)
and on November 7, 2000 received news that she was
pregnant. Avery Zaida Louise was born on July 6, 2001 and is the
first of four fortunate babies. Avery is joined by
Gabriel Aidan Xavier, Alexandra Shannon Moira,
and Everett Oliver Quinn.

Congratulations Caitlin and thank you for your inspiration.

This book is dedicated with love to you.

Photograph courtesy Chadwick Bronson Radunske

With pregnancy becoming more prominently celebrated,
maternity photographer Sandy Jamieson realized the impending need
for a product such as *Zaida Baby – My First Keepsake*. Not only did it provide an
outlet for her passion, but an alternative to the baby books currently
on the market today. Jamieson was interested in creating something that was
classy and contemporary to coincide with the changing times.

While February 2004 officially marks the start of Jamieson's career capturing
bellies and babies, her passion for photography started at the age of fourteen.
Jamieson recognizes the miracle and memorability of the pregnant journey.
Zaida Baby – My First Keepsake allows mothers to preserve all of the pivotal
moments from conception to a child's first birthday while catering
to their emotional and mental thoughts during pregnancy.

"Pregnancy is meant to be celebrated, and *Zaida Baby – My First Keepsake*
displays that pregnancy is no longer something that needs
to be hidden under baggy clothes.
Celebrate the life within you!"

Celebrate *Zaida Baby – My First Keepsake...*
a classy twist on an old tradition!

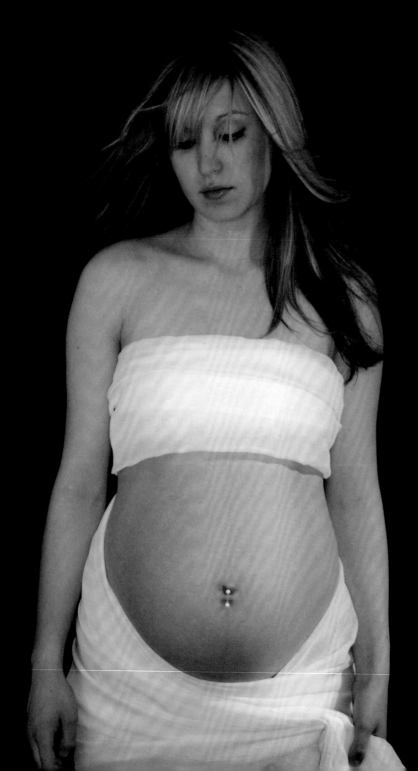

Beautiful baby...
you're my life
my breath
my song.
I'll cherish you
believe in you
love you
forever
my miracle child.

· Emily T. Wierenga

From a Parent's Perspective

Thank you for coming into my life...

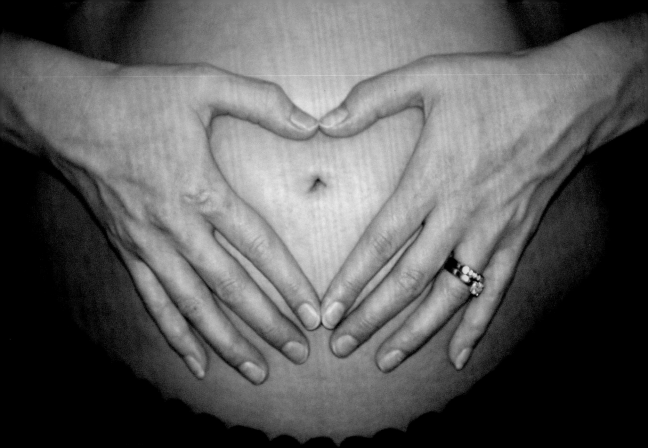

*And for letting me love you
wholeheartedly.*

I promise to nurture

And to teach you things about life that have inspired me.

*I will encourage you
to be an amazing person...*

And to be proud of who you are.

I will trust your decisions...

Whatever those decisions may be.

I will be there when you fall...

Soothe your tears...

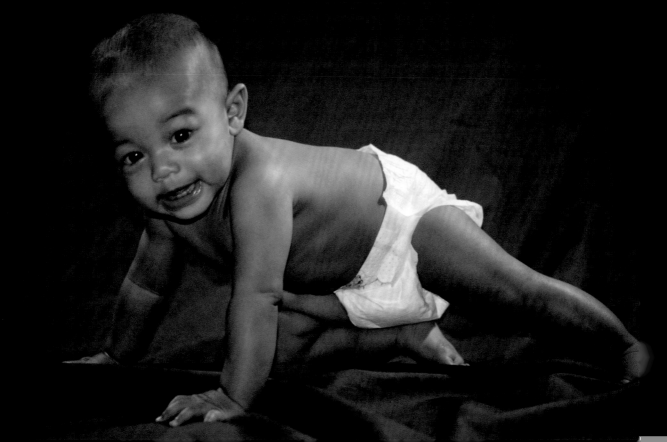

And help you to your feet again.

We will both make mistakes as we embark on this journey together...

And that's okay.

*There is no pressure for you
to be perfect...*

Just strive to be the best that you can be.

I promise to be patient with you...

And to let you grow as an individual.

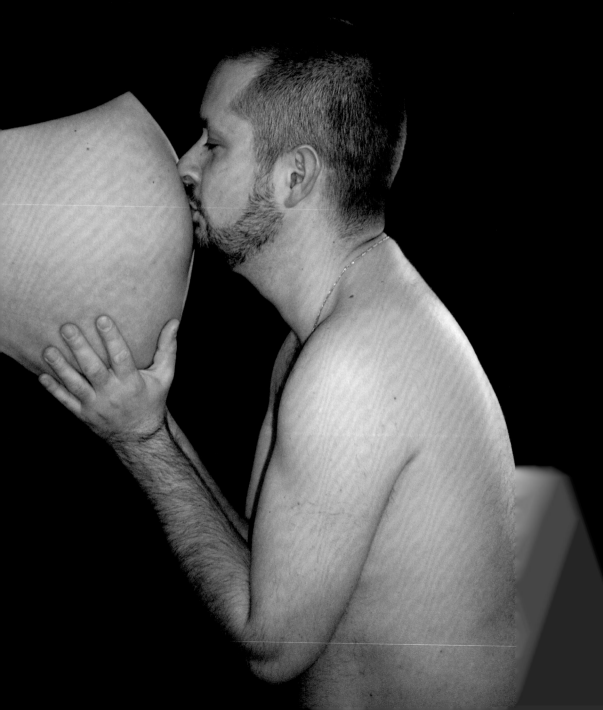

I will affirm you when you doubt yourself...

And forgive you when you speak out in anger or frustration.

I will support your hopes,
your dreams and your talents...

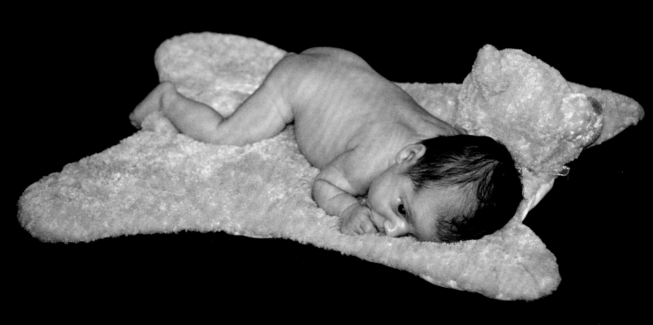

And encourage you to discover things on your own.

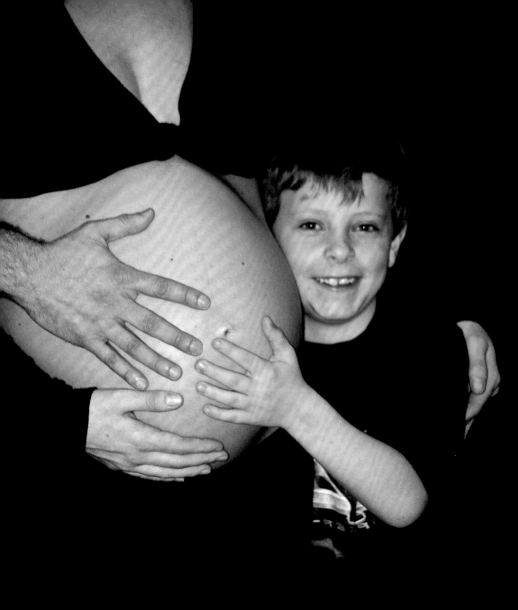

I promise to laugh with you...

Often.

*I will help you to see
the beauty of the outdoors...*

*And inspire you
to explore the world.*

I will get excited about the little things...

*Because little things
are so very special.*

I will respect you as you grow older...

And share with you my wisdom.

I will provide you with warmth...

And comfort...

Balance...

Security...

Friendship...

And love.

But most importantly...

*I will give you
the feeling of family.*

I love you.

Maternity photograph

My Pregnancy Journal

Maternity photograph

"My how you've grown!"

At 5 months my belly was .... cm.

At 6 months my belly was .... cm.

At 7 months my belly was .... cm.

At 8 months my belly was .... cm.

At 9 months my belly was .... cm.

Maternity photograph

Changes I have noticed in my body...

Maternity photograph

The first time I felt you move...

It felt like...

Ultrasound photograph

My first ultrasound was...

Maternity photograph

Maternity photograph

A special letter to my baby...

Baby's photograph

From a Baby's Perspective

My first photograph

Thank you for making me
part of this world.

My name is ....

It is special because ....

I was named after ....

I was born on ....

I weighed .... pounds & .... ounces

and stretched to an amazing .... inches long.

Other names considered ....

....

....

In your arms

Hello world!

A special memory of my birth was...

....

....

....

....

....

....

....

....

....

....

....

....

....

....

....

....

My homecoming

My first day home was on ....

....

I was dressed in ....

....

My address is ....

My nursery décor is ....

....

....

....

Special people

Important people to remember...

My midwife/doctor was ....

....

People present at my birth ....

....

My first visitors were ....

....

....

My first house guests were ....

....

....

Special thanks goes out to ....

....

....

Cheese!

A funny picture of me

My first haircut photograph
(with lock of hair)

My first haircut!

My first haircut was on ....

My stylist's name was ....

at ....

My reaction was ....

....

....

Your reaction was ....

....

....

....

My first birthday photograph

My first birthday!

We celebrated by ....

The decorations were ....

My cake was ....

My reaction was ....

The people at my party were ....

....

....

....

Special gifts given to me ....

....

....

Look at me in the tub!

Other firsts...

My first bath ....

My first smile ....

My first words ....

My first step ....

My first tooth ....

My first vacation ....

The first time I rolled onto my back ....

....

The first time I slept through the night ....

....

The first time I ate by myself ....

....

Photograph of me

My favorite song ....

My favorite story ....

My favorite time of the day ....

My favorite day trip ....

My favorite place to eat ....

My favorite food ....

My favorite animal ....

My favorite sound ....

My favorite toy ....

Photograph of me

Famous sports figures ....

Best-selling books ....

Technological advances ....

Fashion trends ....

Popular songs ....

Famous musicians ....

Blockbuster movies ....

Popular T.V. shows ....

Famous actors ....

World news ....

Photograph of my house

The price of life...

Fuel $ ....

A new car $ ....

A compact disc $ ....

A house $ ....

A computer $ ....

Two tickets to the movies $ ....

A package of diapers $ ....

A loaf of bread $ ....

Photograph of
my grandparents

Family photograph

Family photograph